ILLUMINATION PRESENTS

DESPICABLE ME 3™

ACTIVITY BOOK

DESPICABLE ME 3: ACTIVITY BOOK

A CENTUM BOOK 9781911460428

PUBLISHED IN GREAT BRITAIN BY CENTUM BOOKS LTD

THIS EDITION PUBLISHED 2017

1 3 5 7 9 10 8 6 4 2

CENTUM BOOKS LTD, 20 DEVON SQUARE, NEWTON ABBOT, DEVON, TQ12 2HR, UK

BOOKS@CENTUMBOOKSLTD.CO.UK

CENTUM BOOKS LIMITED REG. NO. 07641486

A CIP CATALOGUE RECORD FOR THIS BOOK IS AVAILABLE FROM THE BRITISH LIBRARY

PRINTED IN CHINA.

FAMILY FOREVER!

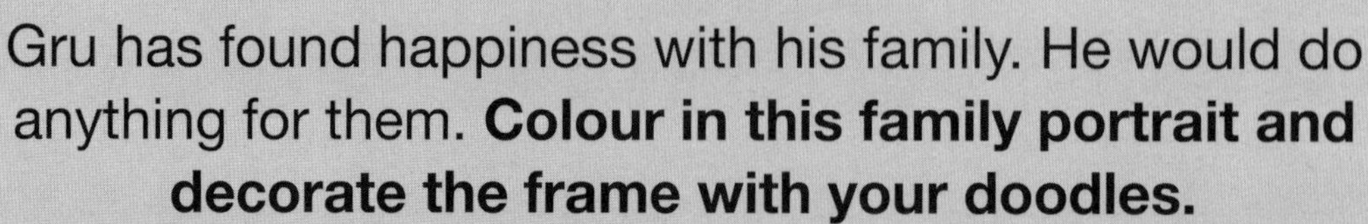

Gru has found happiness with his family. He would do anything for them. **Colour in this family portrait and decorate the frame with your doodles.**

TIKI TIME

The girls throw Lucy and Gru a special Hawaiian-themed party just for them. **Add the finishing touches to the delightful decorations using your colours.**

RECIPE FOR LOVE

Agnes makes Gru and Lucy a wonderful (but completely inedible) soup for their special Hawaiian meal. What concoction would you create for a special occasion? **Draw your ingredients below.**

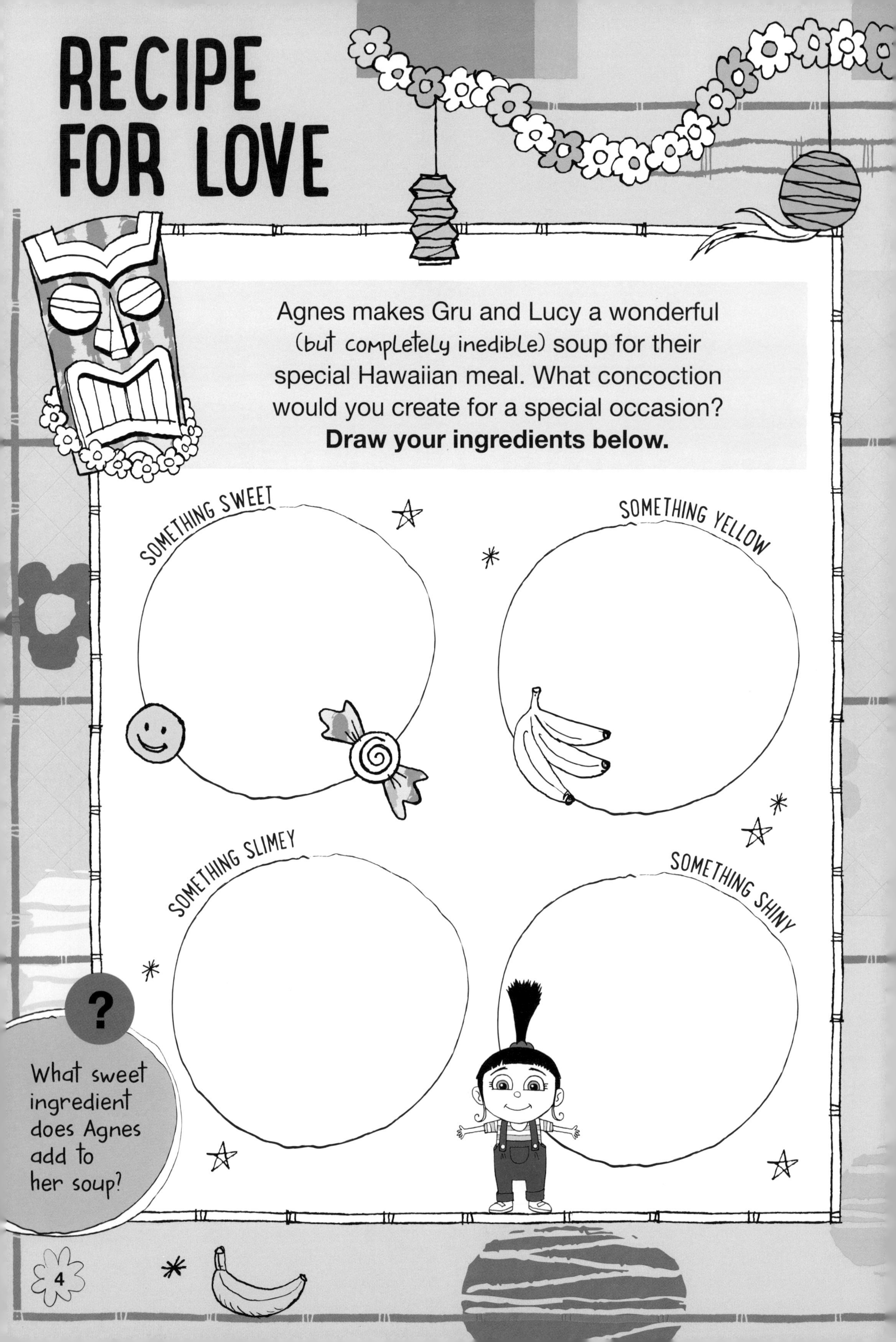

?

What sweet ingredient does Agnes add to her soup?

RECIPE INSTRUCTIONS

Write your recipe instructions on the lines below:

1

2

3

4

5

ARE THERE ANY SPECIAL INSTRUCTIONS? HOW ABOUT HAVING TO DO THE HULA WHILST MIXING?

I ♥ THE 80S!

Balthazar Bratt, former 80s TV child star, lover of shoulder pads and big hair, is as dastardly at heart as his outfits. He's an Evil Genius. **Colour him in, 80s style.**

BALTHAZAR'S COLOURING TIPS:

- USE COLOURS THAT CLASH. THE BRIGHTER THE BETTER – **MAKE IT NEON!**
- PASTELS ARE TRENDY – I LOVE A POWDER BLUE SUIT. **WHO DOESN'T?!**

DREAM UP A NEW GHASTLY HAIRSTYLE FOR BALTHAZAR IN THIS BOX.

MINION MAKEOVER

Now you have been introduced to the wacky world of 80s fashion, **give the Minions an 80s makeover with your colouring pens and pencils.**

DRAW A **BANANA-SHAPED** KEYTAR IN THIS BOX!

BUBBLE TROUBLE

Balthazar Bratt's bubble blaster is really good at blowing bubbles, but at capturing the diamond he's after, not so much.

Can you count all the bubbles on this page?

ANSWERS ON
page 32

CAN YOU FIND THE MASSIVE DIAMOND HE'S AFTER?

CLUE: IT'S THE BIGGEST!

SPOT THE BOT!

Clive the robot is the best sidekick any 80s-loving, keytar-carrying super-villain could ever wish for.

But which bot matches the real Clive? Spot the real bot!

AMONGST CLIVE'S MANY SKILLS IS HIS TALENT FOR BEING ABLE TO PLAY UPON REQUEST ANY 80s TUNE AT ANY TIME.

DANCE MOVES AT THE READY!

ANSWERS ON page 32

UNICORN LOVE
Agnes' love for unicorns knows no bounds, except when it comes to family. So much so that Agnes puts her beloved unicorn up for sale when she thinks it will help them. That's love! Colour in this page!
How much do you love UNICORNS?
What do you love most? Draw it here.

DESIGN A UNICORN!

Sometimes all you need in life is a fluffy unicorn to be happy. Just ask Agnes, she knows! **Draw and colour your own unicorn in this frame.**

AGNES' TIPS

* Unicorns love to be loved so draw with LOVE!
* Use your favourite colours to make it extra-special.
* Think of someone you love while you draw!

MY UNICORN IS CALLED:

LOOK WITH LUCY

Study these two gadget-packed pictures featuring Lucy's spy tech.

What's in the first picture, but not in the second?

?

Q: What's a spy's favourite game?

A: Eye-spy!

ANSWERS ON
PAGE 32

80s SUDOKU

Balthazar Bratt is obsessed by the 80s! **Can you complete the 80s style Sudoku puzzles below?**

WHAT TO DO:

Colour in the squares so that each colour only appears once in every column, row or square.

1

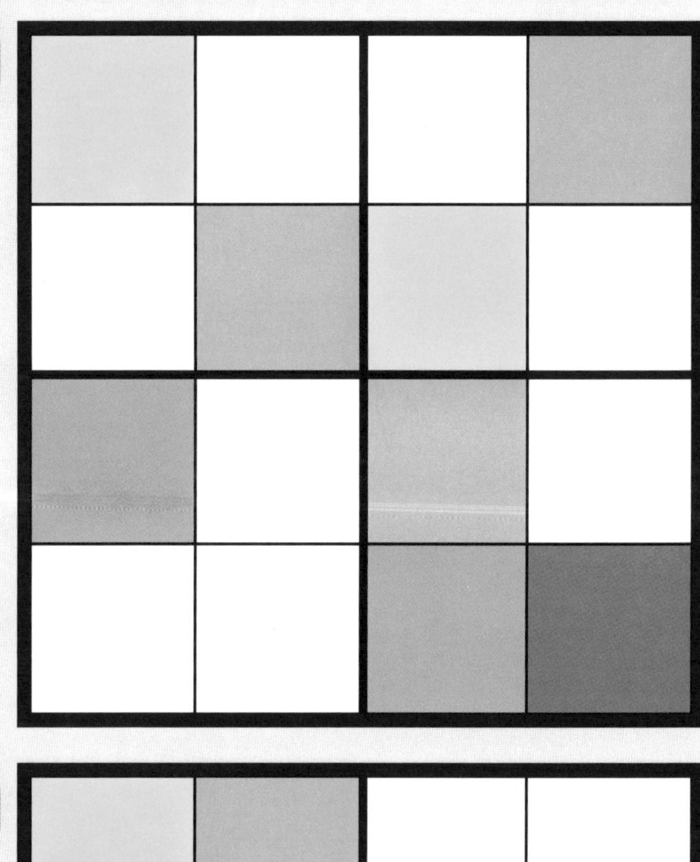

2

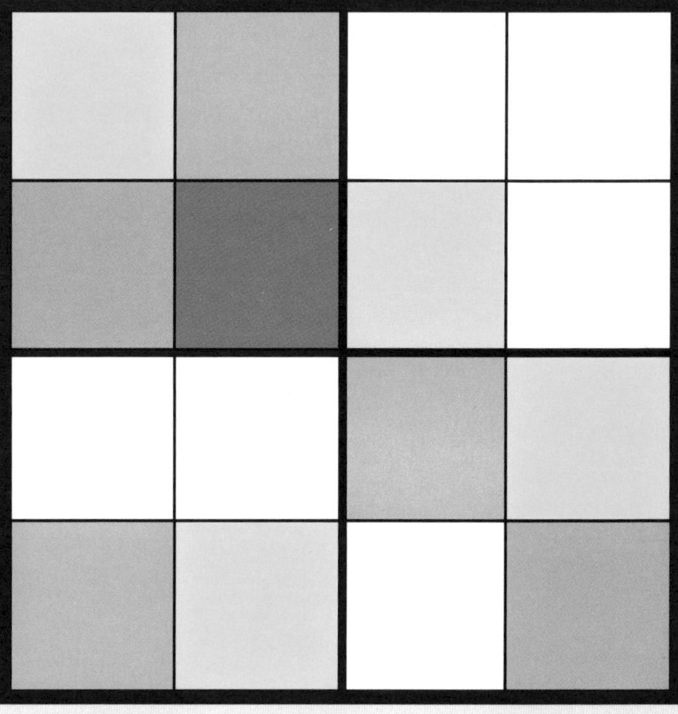

ANSWERS ON
PAGE 32

GRU VS DRU

Gru discovers he has a long-lost twin brother called Dru. Despite their similarity in looks (well, almost, just look at their hair!) they are quite different from one another.

Colour them in!

MATCH THESE FACTS TO THE CORRECT TWIN:

1. Surrounds himself with small pink creatures that go "Oink!"
2. Is a reformed super-villain, turned super-spy.
3. Loves to dress all in white.
4. Recently got fired from his job.
5. Likes to drive a red sporty number.

ANSWERS ON PAGE 32

FOREST QUEST

Agnes is on a quest for a **unicorn** in the forest. But what sort of animal does she find at the end?

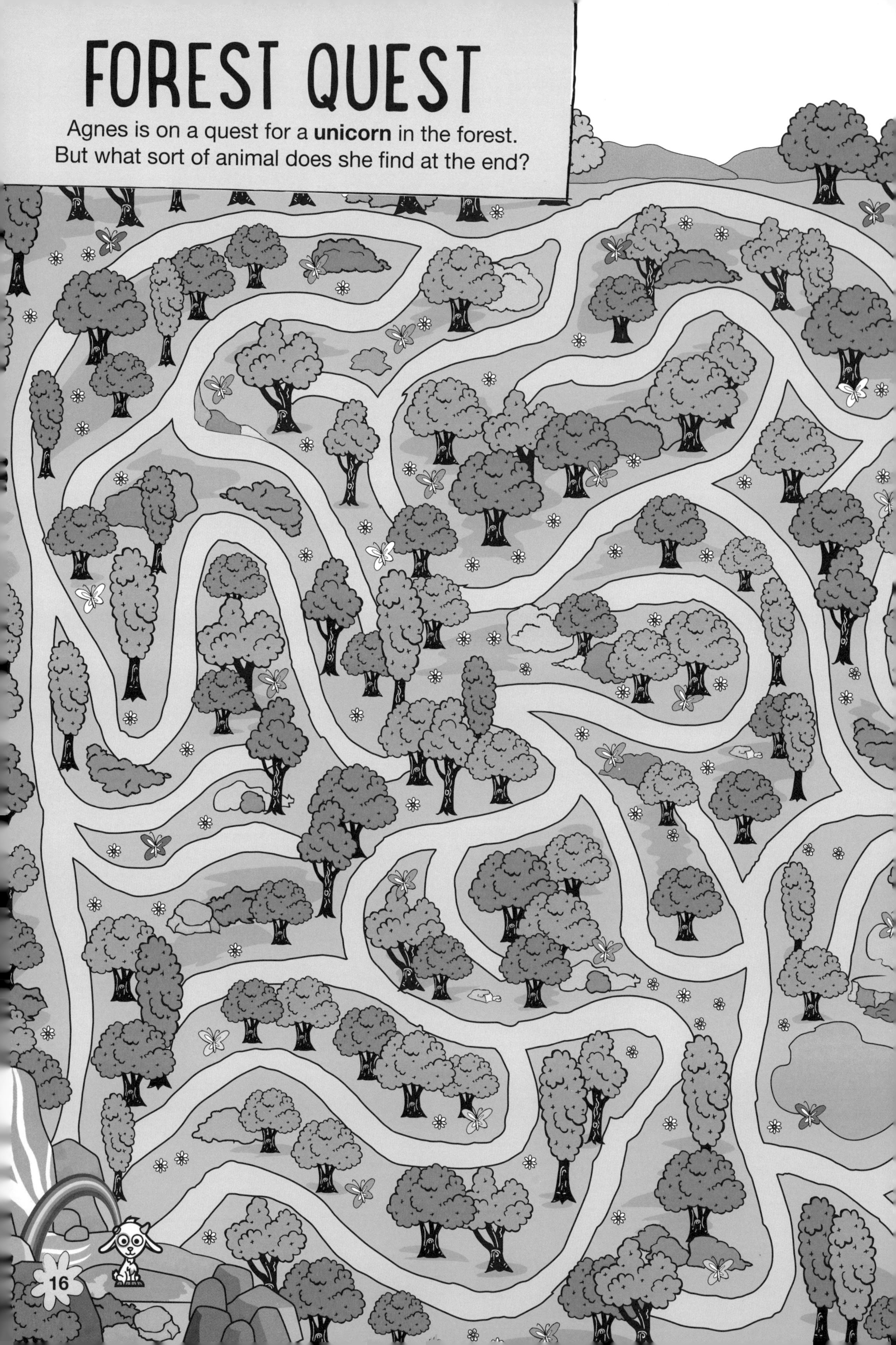

How many pink butterflies does Agnes find on the way? ?

ANSWERS ON PAGE 32

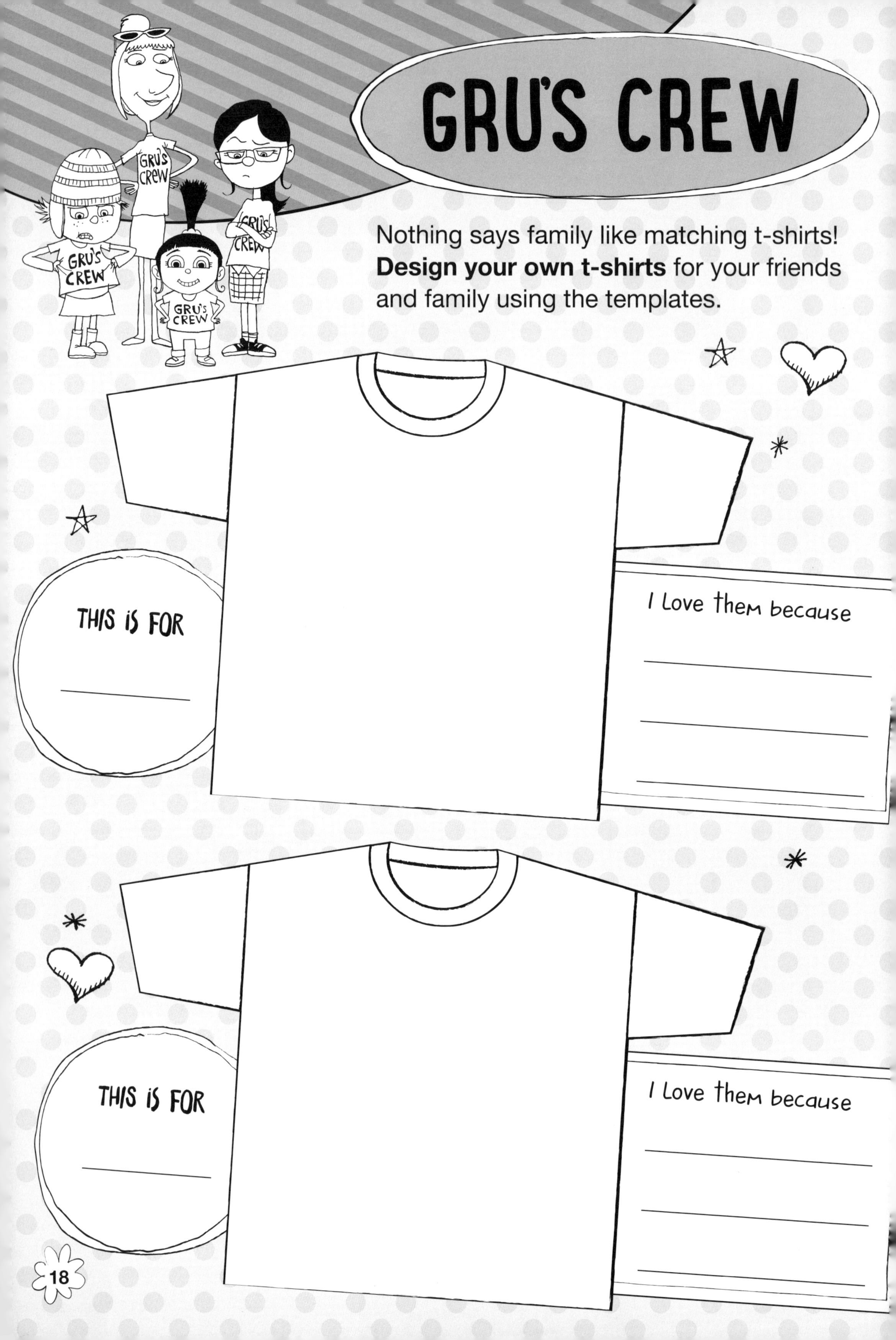

GRU'S CREW

Nothing says family like matching t-shirts! **Design your own t-shirts** for your friends and family using the templates.

THIS IS FOR ____________

I Love them because
____
____
____

THIS IS FOR ____________

I Love them because
____
____
____

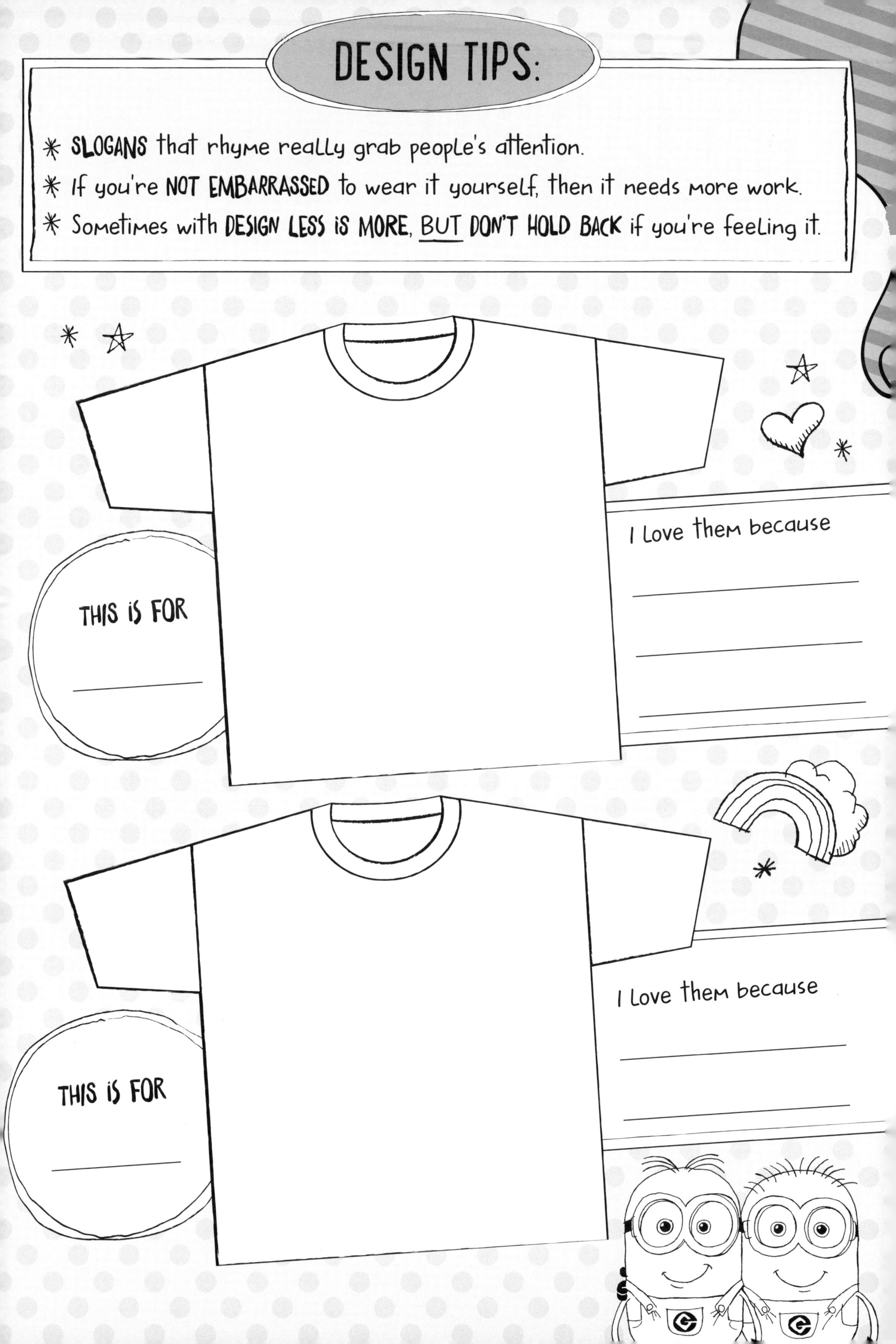
DESIGN TIPS:
* SLOGANS that rhyme really grab people's attention.
* If you're NOT EMBARRASSED to wear it yourself, then it needs more work.
* Sometimes with DESIGN LESS IS MORE, BUT DON'T HOLD BACK if you're feeling it.
THIS IS FOR
I love them because
THIS IS FOR
I love them because

WHO DUNNIT?

One of these Minions has been up to no good.

Can you use the clues below to work out which one in the line-up it is?

CLUES

1. He's not holding a banana.
2. He's not very tall.
3. He has one eye.
4. He's not looking straight ahead.

D E F

3'0"
2'6"
2'0"
1'6"
1'0"
0'6"

ANSWERS ON PAGE 32

MATCHING MINIONS

Despite appearances and the matching uniforms, there are eight differences between the two Minion pictures below. **Can you circle them all?**

MIXED-UP LETTERS

The Minions are planning something. **Can you unscramble letters below to work out what it is they are up to?**

C E P E A S

ANSWERS ON PAGE 32

RAINBOW UNICORN

Give Agnes' unicorn a rainbow makeover with your colouring pens and pencils, then **colour in the rainbows** all around!

CAN YOU MAKE TEN NEW WORDS USING THE LETTERS **UNICORN**?

1 ____________________
2 ____________________
3 ____________________
4 ____________________
5 ____________________
6 ____________________
7 ____________________
8 ____________________
9 ____________________
10 ____________________

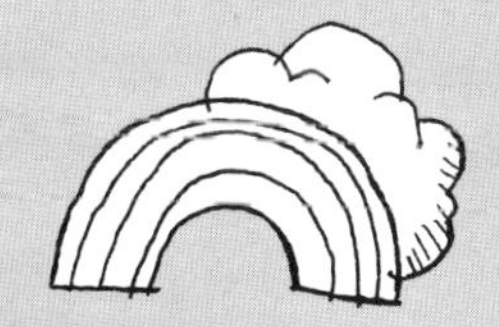

UNICORN YOUR STUFF!

Colour in this book cover, then cut it out and stick it on your favourite notebook or diary.

Ask a grown-up to help when using scissors!

* Scissors
* A blank notebook
* Glue or double-sided tape

WHAT TO DO:

* Colour in the book cover – give it some magic and sparkle!
* Cut out this page, then cut out the book cover using scissors following the dashed lines.
* Use glue or double-sided tape to stick the cover to a notebook or diary.
* Fill your notebook with unicorn dreams and wishes!

BIG PIG, LITTLE PIG

Freedonia is wonderful place to live, if you like pigs and cheese. **Can you complete the seek and find challenges and search this pig-filled scene?**

CAN YOU FIND?

1. The biggest pig
2. The smallest pig
3. The stripy pig
4. The pig sat on cheese
5. The pig with a Minion riding it
6. The pig that looks a bit scared

ANSWERS ON PAGE 32

CHEESY SEQUENCES

Margo just doesn't get Freedonia. What's the love of cheese about? And why is there so much of it? **Work out which piece of cheese comes next in the sequences** using the pieces in the box below, before Margo gets even more cheesed off.

?

?

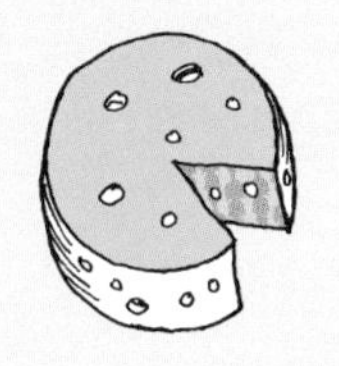

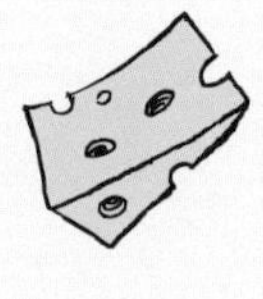
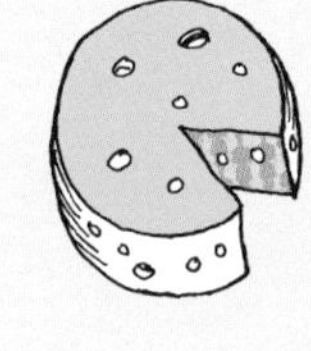

?

?

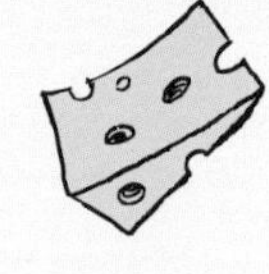

?

WHICH PIECE OF CHEESE FITS?

A 

B 

C 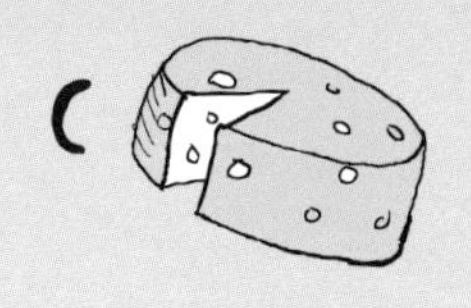

ANSWERS ON PAGE 32

SUPER-MAGIC HORN!

Follow the instructions to create your very own magical unicorn horn. Perfect for fancy-dress events or for your everyday unicorn needs.

Ask a grown-up to help when using scissors!

* Scissors
* String or ribbon
* Glue
* Thick card
* A pencil
* Colouring pens or

Colour in your unicorn horn in your most magical colours.

Cut out the opposite page, then carefully cut out the unicorn horn using scissors.

Use glue to stick the horn to thick card, then carefully cut around the horn.

Use a pencil to push through the two holes at each end.

Push two pieces of string or ribbon, about 30 cm each in length, through each hole. Tie a knot on each to fix in place.

Place the horn on your forehead, then wrap the string or ribbon around the back and tie together.

PRACTISE YOUR DESIGNS ON THESE FIRST:

TIP

Use the practice box to try out some designs!

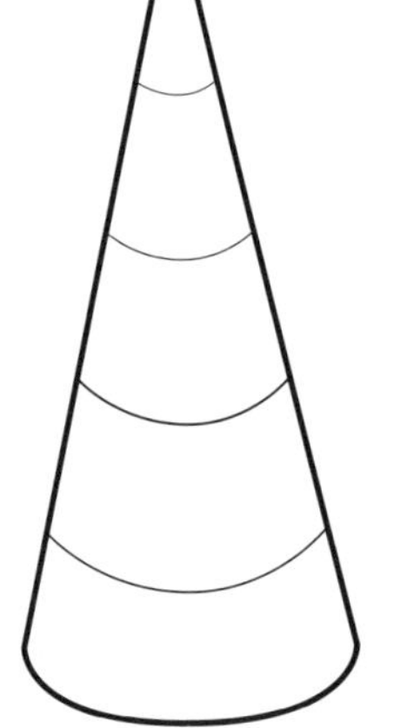

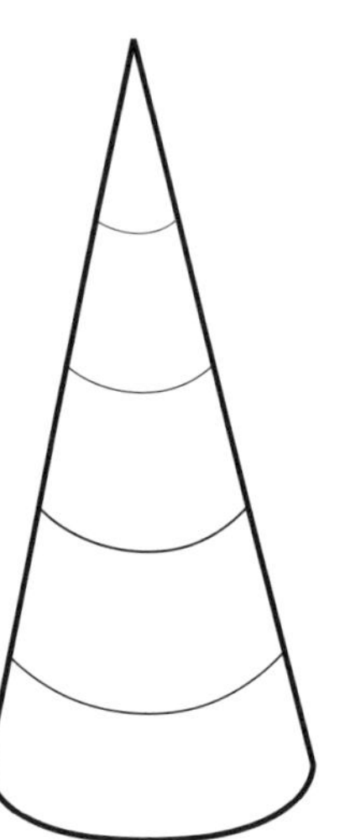

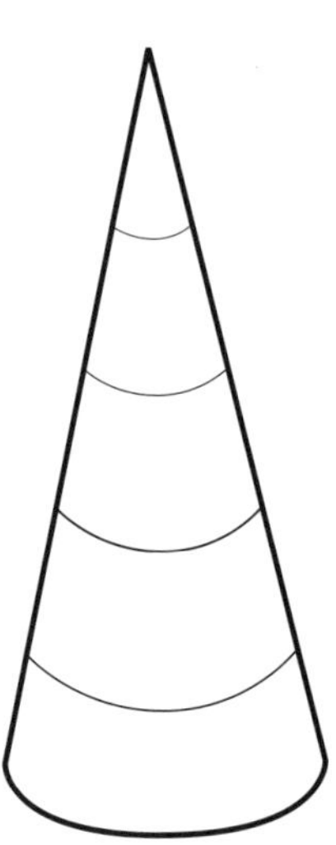

TIP
ASK SOMEONE TO HELP YOU TIE THE ENDS TOGETHER – IT CAN BE TRICKY!

Families come in all shapes and sizes, just like Gru's. **Can you spot eight differences between these two family pictures?** Circle each difference and colour in a heart when you find one!

ANSWERS ON PAGE 32

UNICORN MOBILE

How about adding some actual sparkle to your mobile using glue and glitter?

Follow the instructions to make this wonderful unicorn mobile that is both Agnes and unicorn approved.

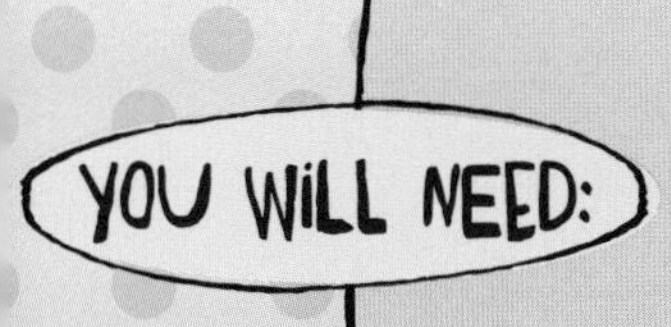

- Scissors
- Five pieces of string or riibbon of equal length, approx. 30 cm.
- Glue or double-sided tape
- Colouring pens or pencils

Ask a grown-up to help when using scissors!

1

Press out the three card pieces and the little press-outs of your unicorn mobile.

2

Colour in the press-out pieces in your favourite colours.

TIP
Ask someone to help you tie the knots – it can be tricky!

3

Press out the little holes on the main pieces, this is where the ribbon or string will be threaded through.

4

Join the main pieces together by threading string through the holes and tying a knot behind to secure in place.

5

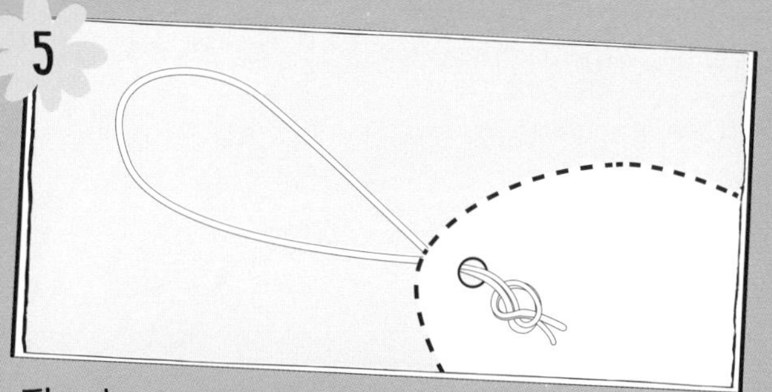

The top hole is used for hanging your mobile. Take the fifth piece of string and create a loop.

6

Use glue or double-sided tape to attach the stars, hearts and face to the string.

CODED COLOURING

Whether your heart is on the side of spy or villain, one thing's for sure, you're going to need a lot of gadgets.

Use the code below to colour in the gadgets.
Just watch out for the Fart Blaster!

COLOUR CODE

* Pink # Blue ° Yellow • Purple □ Orange x Red

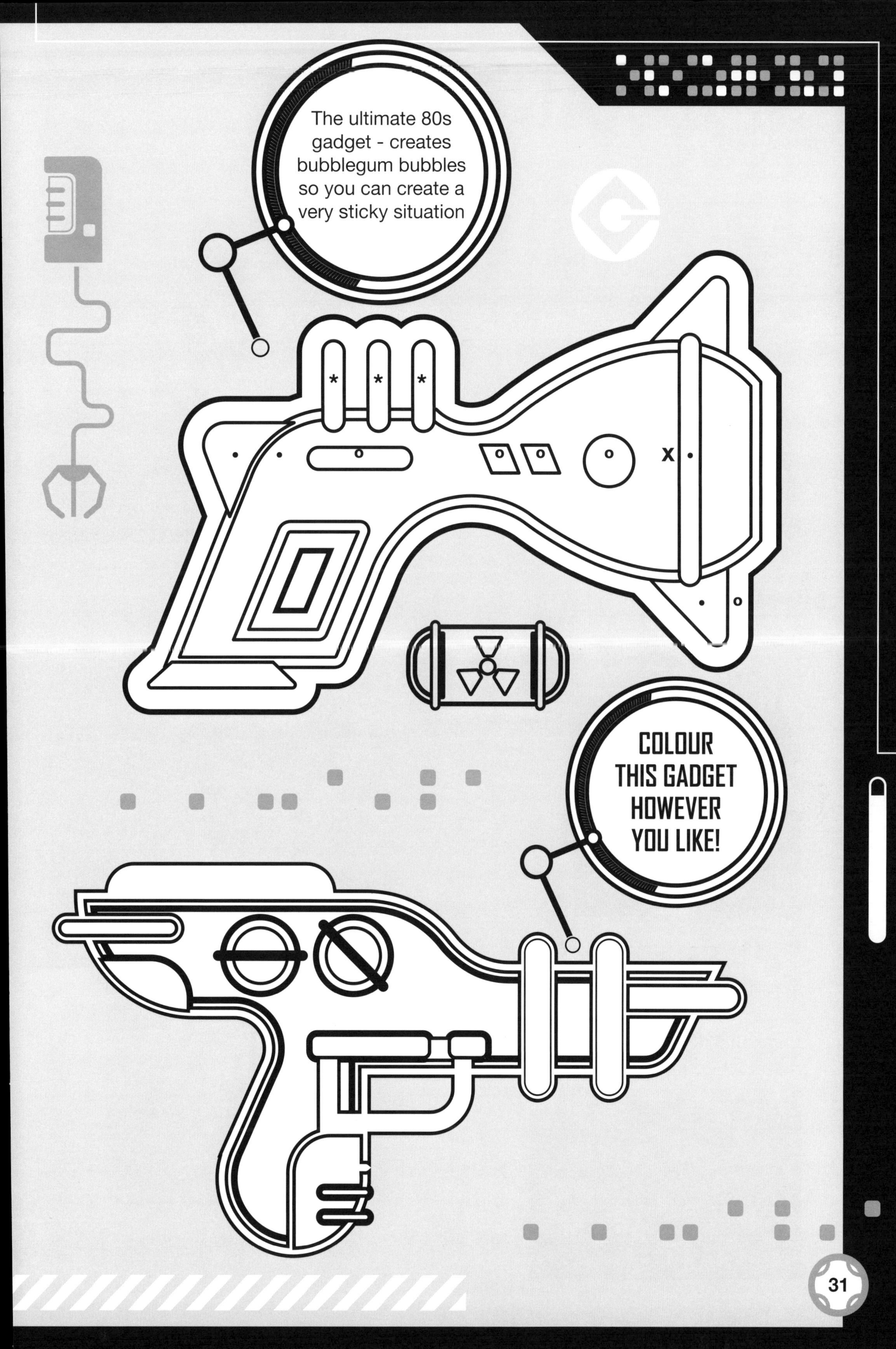
The ultimate 80s gadget - creates bubblegum bubbles so you can create a very sticky situation
COLOUR THIS GADGET HOWEVER YOU LIKE!

ANSWERS

Page 4
Agnes adds sweets to her soup.

Page 8
There are 42 bubbles.

Page 9
Bot 2 matches the real Clive.

Page 12

Page 13

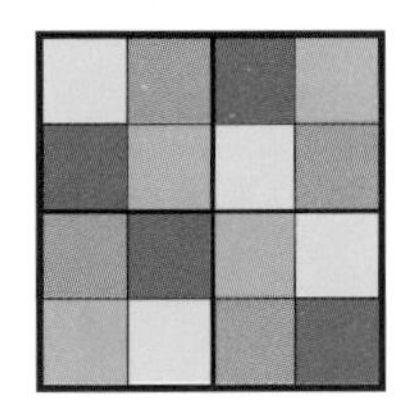
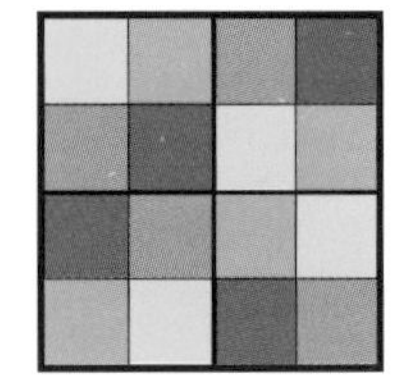

Page 15
1: DRU, **2:** GRU, **3:** DRU,
4: GRU, **5:** DRU.

Page 16 & 17
Agnes finds **7** pink butterflies on the way.

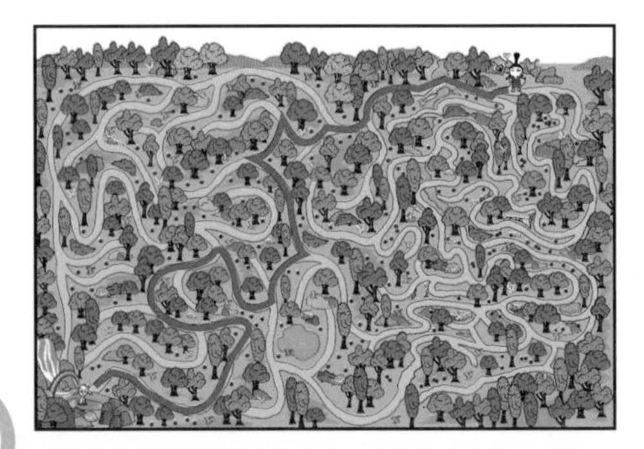

Page 20
Minion B

Page 21
The Minions are planning their **ESCAPE.**

Page 22
Here are some we found: IN, NO, ON, OR, INN, RUN, URN, COIN, CORN, ICON, IRON, NOUN, RUIN, UNION.

Page 24

Page 25
1: B; **2:** C; **3:** A; **4:** C; **5:** B.

Page 28